Specimen Sight-Reading Tests for Trumpet and Brass Band instruments 𝄞

(excluding Trombone 𝄞)

Trumpet, Cornet, Flugelhorn, E♭ Horn, Baritone 𝄞, Euphonium 𝄞, Tuba 𝄞

Grades 1-5

The Associated Board of
the Royal Schools of Music

GRADE 1

AB 2484

Allegretto

13

Moderato

14

Moderato

15

Andante

16

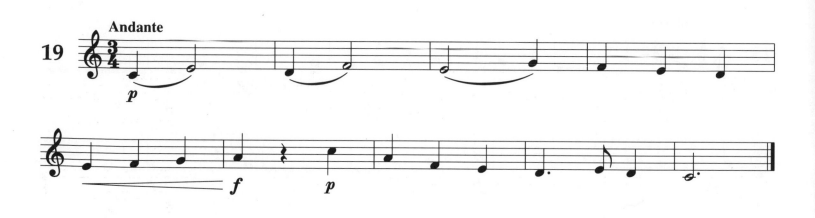

GRADE 2

AB 2484

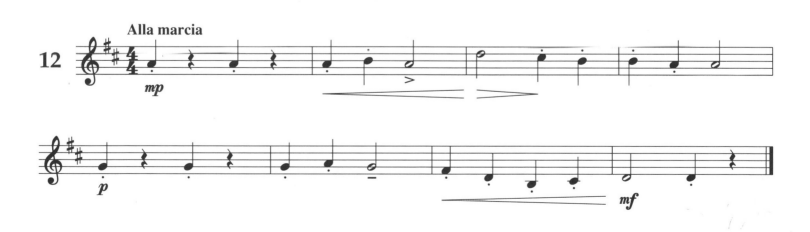

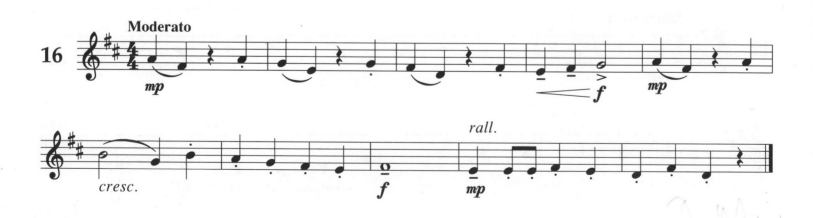

17 Andante

18 Allegro

19 Moderato

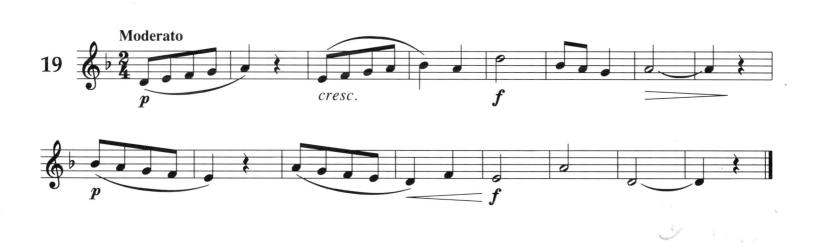

20 Allegro

GRADE 3

GRADE 4

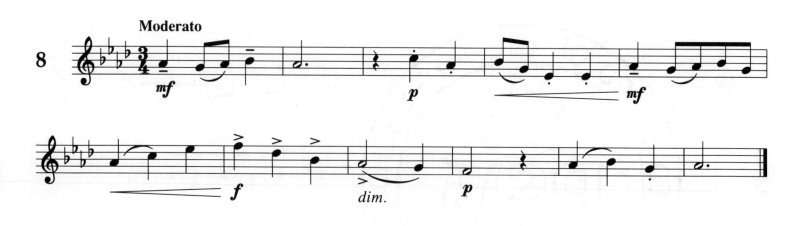

Tempo giusto

Risoluto

Alla marcia

Moderato

24

AB 2484

Printed and bound in Great Britain by
Caligraving Limited Thetford Norfolk 3:07